MACMILLAN READERS
STARTER LEVEL

JULES VERNE

Around the World in Eighty Days

Retold by María José Lobo
and Pepita Subirà

Phileas Fogg's journey around the world

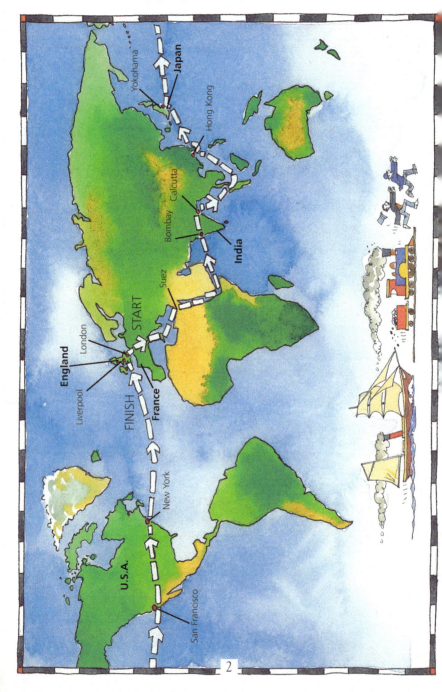

Phileas Fogg is a member of the Reform Club. He goes to the Club every day at 11.30 a.m. At the Club he reads newspapers and books. He also plays cards. Today it is Wednesday, 2nd October, 1872 …

Their train arrives in New York at 11.15 in the evening. They are too late for the ship to Liverpool. They go to a hotel. The next morning …

Where are you going?

To Bordeaux, in France. But I don't want any passengers.

I can pay you eight thousand dollars. Please take us on your ship!

Well … OK. We leave at 9 o'clock.

Phileas Fogg arrives in Liverpool at 11.40 on 21st December. At 11.41 Detective Fix touches Mr Fogg's shoulder.

We are in Britain now. I am a detective. I am arresting you. You will go to prison.

Welcome to Liverpool

Why?

Because you are the missing bank robber. You have got £55,000 in your bag. The money is from the Bank of England.

What do you mean? I'm not a robber.